Ghost in My Room

Taylor Sapp

Alphabet Publishing

Contents

Before You Read

1. Do you believe in ghosts? Why or why not?

2. Some cultures believe ghosts are mostly good, others that ghosts are evil, still others that ghosts can be both. What do people believe in your culture about ghosts?

3. What would you do if there was a ghost in your apartment or house

4. In many ghost stories, a ghost haunts a particular person or place. Why would a ghost do that?

Ghost in My Room

Paul loved his new apartment. It was located in the heart of Brooklyn, a very popular part of New York City. The one-bedroom studio apartment was small, 500 square feet, but that was normal for New York. The whole thing was covered from top to bottom with beautiful old wood. And it was on the 13th floor of a historic old building. It had a lot of style. It had even come with furniture!

And, most importantly, it was cheap!

He'd just graduated from studying art at Iowa State, near the farmlands where he grew up. Now Paul's dream of making an impact with art was starting to come true! A few months after graduation, he'd gotten an offer to work for an advertising company as a graphic design artist in New York City. He'd been so excited, until he arrived and started apartment-hunting!

Unfortunately, New York City was not cheap! And entry-level graphic design jobs did not pay that much. He didn't have any family or friends nearby. Being something of a shy artist, he didn't want to live with roommates. The hostel he was staying at was cheap but very uncomfortable.

But just as Paul had given up hope, he got a mysterious text with a link to the address that simply said: "An apartment so cheap it's scary."

· · · · ● · ● · · ·

So now Paul sat with his sketchbook on the couch that had come free with his new apartment. He was drawing the sights from outside his window: a parade of giant skyscrapers in the distance, the traffic below, the reflection of a woman's face in the window …

"Wait a minute!" Paul jumped up and looked behind him, but there was no woman. He looked again at the window. The reflection was now gone.

"I shouldn't have had those beers to celebrate," he said to himself as he sat down and started sketching again.

• • • ● • ● • ● • •

At work the next week, Paul was lost on his computer making a banner for a client's website when a head popped into his office door.

"Hey, friend." It was Ping, an annoying, chatty young woman about his age, and the one person who liked to disrupt his focus.

"Heard you found an apartment in the old Williamson Building?"

Paul nodded.

"Nice! I just hope it wasn't the 13th floor."

Though she clearly had more to say, when Paul didn't say anything, Ping put her head back down and didn't continue the conversation.

That night, Paul was lying awake, thinking about the nice things his boss had said about his work today. So it was a while before he became aware of the soft moaning.

And when he did notice it, Paul became very still, listening and trying to figure out where it was coming from. It was a soft sound, too quiet to hear if he moved. But it was definitely human and it sounded sad. Where was it coming from?

He walked to the window, but the sound was quieter there. He walked to the door. Same thing. He put his ear to the walls, and heard nothing in the apartments next to his. No, this moaning was definitely coming from his apartment.

"Hello?" he said quietly.

No answer.

Paul was startled but he didn't know what to do. So he ignored it. For a while it seemed like it had disappeared. But when he climbed into bed later, the apartment was so quiet, he could hear it again. Unable to block the noise out or stop his brain from getting scared, he took a sleeping pill.

• • • • ● • ● • • •

The next day, as he was eating a tuna sandwich at his desk, he felt someone in the office with him. He turned to see Ping sitting in her chair in the entry to his working space, salad in a little container sitting in her lap. Somehow, she'd quietly moved her chair on wheels from her office to his.

"Can I join you?" It was a little late to ask.

"No," he wanted to say, but instead he said nothing.

"The tuna looks good. Did you get it at the sandwich place across the street? That place is good. Anyway, how's the new apartment treating you?"

"Fine."

"You are on the 13th floor, aren't you?"

He didn't answer.

"That's the only reason you'd be able to afford an apartment there. Me too, I looked at it, but then I heard all the stories, and I was like, 'No thank you' and even though my brother is kind of a jerk, as long as I help pay for food, he never charges me rent!"

Paul knew he should try to be friendly. He could ask her a question, let her talk about her background, where she was from, why she was living with her brother, or something. He just didn't want to. And he had a feeling she would keep talking no matter what he said.

So he said nothing, and after a short pause, she continued anyway.

"In case you're wondering, actually my family is from Nebraska, but my brother and I both studied at New York University, and then, he's the older one, so he got a job and apartment..."

As she kept going, Paul felt confused. He wanted to end the conversation and think about his work, but he was interested in the strange comments about his apartment. He suddenly interrupted her, "What are the stories you've heard about the 13th floor?"

Ping smiled at him. "If I tell you, I don't think you'll want to live there..." Although he hoped she wouldn't, she continued. "But have you seen any ghosts?"

Paul laughed. "I don't believe in that stuff."

"Are you sure you haven't seen or heard anything?"

· · · ● · ● · ● · · ·

A few days passed. Nothing strange happened and Paul had almost forgotten about any ghost talk.

But one night, as he was brushing his teeth after a hot shower, a note suddenly appeared on the mirror, written in the steam: GET OUT!

Paul was terrified. "Who's there?" he managed to say weakly. For a minute he considered running, screaming out into the night in his towel and never coming back. Instead, after a few more frozen minutes of silence, he quickly got in his pajamas, climbed into bed, sat so his back was against the wall, and wrapped the covers around him like a blanket. He didn't turn off the light and he didn't plan to sleep. But he ended up waiting for nothing and finally fell asleep in the early morning.

· · · ● · ● · ● · · ·

The next day at work, he told Ping what he'd seen. He couldn't help feeling scared. He told her not to tell anyone else. But Ping was not the type who could keep secrets.

Soon after, everyone in the office was making fun of Paul. Ghost Boy, they called him. And even Paul was starting to doubt himself. Maybe he was just stressed. Or exhausted. He couldn't remember the last time he'd slept normally. He had just about decided the whole thing was his brain playing tricks on him until something happened a few weeks later.

As Paul was eating dinner, there was a knock at the door.

Was he surprised to see Ping with a strange expression on her face. "I felt bad for gossiping about you. But I believe you! I've heard too many stories about this place! So I thought I should come over and see if I could help get rid of the ghost."

Ping made her way in and stretched out on the couch. "Quite cozy. I think I could easily spend the night here. Let's see if I can scare that ghost away!"

Paul spoke in an annoyed voice, "I really don't think it's a good idea." He stood near the door, which he was still holding open, still thinking about how he felt about ghost stories. And about Ping. As usual, Ping never allowed him a moment's pause.

She turned to him and said, "Look. You may not like me. But I'm the only one who believes you. So let's work together to get rid of this ghost."

"What's in it for you?" Paul asked.

"Well, believe it or not, I don't have a lot of friends at the office," Ping replied.

"GET OUT!!!" Suddenly, a scream like a police siren made Ping fall off the couch onto the floor as Paul froze in place.

After a moment of silence, Ping's head popped up from the front of the couch.

He wanted to ask if she were ok, but she was looking at something to her left. Then she gasped and covered her mouth. Paul turned to see what she was looking at. In the kitchen on the refrigerator he had a dry-erase board where he kept his shopping list. He could see that the words GET OUT were being written on it by a pen suspended in air.

Paul also looked a little surprised. "I haven't seen that before."

"This is crazy!" Ping screamed!

"I thought you said you'd heard stories about this kind of stuff?"

"Yeah, but not like this! More like sounds of doors opening at night, or weird shapes in the window that disappear. I didn't think there were actual ghosts!"

"Huh? I thought that's why you came here."

"I just said that because I thought you were cute! But this is really scary!"

Paul shrugged. Seeing Ping losing it made him feel strangely calm.

Suddenly the words GET OUT OR DIE appeared reflected in the windows of the living room. Then they heard loud laughter.

Ping screamed, "OK, OK. We'll leave! Just please don't kill us!"

Paul slammed the front door, which had still been open all this time, shut.

"What are you talking about? I don't want to leave! This apartment was a really good deal. I won't have anywhere else to go!"

"You can stay with me and my brother. We have a couch."

"No way! You said you were coming here to help me. You want us to be friends. Or more? Then help me do something about this!"

Although still shaking, Ping stood up and walked over to Paul. She grabbed his shoulder, to support him and to get support from him. Then she stood up as tall as she could, and put on a brave face.

"You know, you're right," she said, "Hey Ghost! Let's talk about this. My friend, or maybe my boyfriend, we're still talking it over. ...But the point is: we need you to be more understanding. Maybe you can talk to us and tell us WHY you want us to get out! Otherwise, no deal. In fact, you get out!"

Paul looked at her, kind of impressed at how fast she'd gone from terrified to terrifying! "Do you really think that'll work?"

As if in answer, there was a strange whispering noise and a bright white light appeared in the middle of the room.

Ping shrieked and got on her knees with her palms together raised in the air as if begging, "OK, ok, I'm sorry, please don't hurt us!"

The light began taking the shape of a human being. He could see through her still, but he could also see the details of her face and body. She was young, close to their age, short hair in a ponytail, and wearing some sort of simple white clothes. She looked sad and angry at the same time. Paul was sure it was the woman he'd seen in the window before.

"Ok," the ghost spoke in a soft voice that was nevertheless full of emotion, "I will tell you and then you will leave!"

"If the story is convincing." Ping responded.

"Or I will kill you."

The threat was less convincing coming from a petite 20-something woman, but Paul and Ping still shuddered.

"My name is Lily Brown. I used to live here with the most wonderful man, Joshua. He was one of the greatest painters in New York, ten times greater than Jackson Pollock or Mark Rothko, but few recognized his talent. He never became rich or famous! I was a sculptor, and his assistant. And one day we fell in love! We lived here and created great art together for years. We were so happy!

"Then, one day he was hired by a cousin of the Rockefeller family. He'd bought a huge country house in Vermont and he wanted Joshua to fill the house with paintings. Joshua wanted to create the paintings at the house, painting the local trees and mountains.

"I had a job of my own. I couldn't leave New York. He said when he came back, we'd have enough money to get married. I couldn't believe it! So I waited and waited, but he never came! I couldn't reach him by phone and the man who hired him disappeared too! After a while I stopped going out, or eating, or doing anything. I will wait for him, forever."

"And when was that?" Ping asked.

"May 20."

"Last year?"

"1955. So now I've told you my story. No one, no one except my dear Joshua is allowed to stay here. I must keep this place for him! I don't care if it takes a thousand years! Now you must go or die!"

Ping and Paul looked at each other.

"I think you're bluffing. You don't sound like a killer." Paul said.

Lily began weeping!

Ping tried to wrap her arm around the ghost's shoulders but failed. Her arm just moved through the air. So Ping settled for holding her arm in the air near the ghost. "I can understand your heartbreak. But do you know what year it is? I don't think Joshua can come back..."

Suddenly Lily looked up with anger. "I don't care! Even if he's a ghost. He must have waited for me. He will come!"

"Well... maybe we can help you find him." Ping said.

"What?" Paul and Lily said at the same time.

"Yeah, look Paul and I are artists too. And we're both falling in love so it'd be perfect to have a ghost couple and a living couple here together."

"Don't get ahead of yourself." Paul said.

"You should be nicer to her," Lily said glaring at him. Then she turned to Paul. "Men can be such jerks."

Ping nodded, "So will you let us help you?"

"I guess so. It has been a bit lonely."

"See? Aren't you glad I came?" Ping gave Paul a kiss on the cheek.

The ghost sighed. "I hope you don't make me regret my decision."

• • • • ● • ● • • •

A few months later, things were looking up for everyone in the apartment. Ping had moved in, almost as happy to be moving out as her brother was. Paul's work continued to be praised by his boss. The jokes about ghost boy faded and he was instead given a new nickname, Picasso, due to his abstract yet creative designs.

And as for the ghost? A trip to the library and some Googling solved the mystery. Joshua had gone to Vermont and lived in the mansion with the businessman. Unfortunately, one night during a wind storm, a tree came down and destroyed the wing where Joshua was staying. By coincidence, a tree also fell on the businessman while he was pulling out of the driveway that night. Because the house was isolated back in the woods far from any town, it was months before they were discovered. Joshua's ghost didn't know how to get back to New York City. So he was still waiting and waiting, hoping to return to Lily even 70 years later!

The people who bought the house were not happy. Joshua never meant to haunt them, but they could feel that there was a ghost in the house. And they were not happy! There were strange noises at night, footsteps in empty rooms, and sights of his face reflected in windows sometimes. When Ping and Paul called them, they were happy to get rid of their ghost. So Ping and Paul drove up to Vermont and convinced Joshua to come with them!

Now with two couples sharing the apartment, one alive, one dead, things were getting a bit crowded. But for cheap rent in New York, it was worth a few problems.

Glossary

afford: have enough money to buy something

bluffing: pretending to be something you aren't

graphic designer: a person who designs documents, logos, and websites on computers

jerk: a foolish or mean person

petite: short and small, usually used to describe women

sculptor: a person who creates three-dimensional art

shrieked: screamed loudly

sketchbook: a book of blank pages that artists draw in

skyscrapers: very tall buildings

startled: surprised or scared

gasped: breathed out air quickly in surprise or excitement

glaring: staring at someone with anger

moaning: making soft low sound like a ghost

shrugged: moved shoulders up and down to show lack of knowledge

shuddered: shook quickly out of fear or cold

sketching: drawing quickly without much detail

weeping: crying loudly

chatty: enjoys talking

isolated: far away from other things

After You Read

1. Why did Paul move to New York? What problem did he face at first?

2. Why did Paul choose this apartment? What did he like about it?

3. What strange things happened in the apartment?

4. What did Paul think about Ping at the beginning of the story? How did those feelings change?

5. What problems did Paul face at work?

6. What problems did Ping face at work and at home?

7. Who is Lily Adams and how did she end

up in the apartment?

8. Who is Joseph and what happened to him?

9. What arrangement did Paul, Ping, Lily, and Joseph make at the end?

10. What would you do if your apartment was haunted?

11. If you dieed

12. Do you think this story is a comedy, a horror story, or something else?

- How would you rewrite it to make it scarier?

- How would you rewrite it to make it funnier?

-

Writing

Write what happens next.

- How does Ping and Paul's relationship work out?

- How does Joshua and Lily's relationship go?

- How do the couples co-exist in the same apartment?

- What problems do they face?

More Readers

Baby Shopping
Changes
Empathy
English Class on Mars
Ghost in My Room
Magic Employment Agency
Rebirth
Attack of the Sleep Demon
The AI Therapist
Thought Police
Time Travel Research: Genghis Khan
Virtual Unreality

AlphabetPublish.com/Book-Category/
Graded-Reader